10 Minute Tales

The Pontypandy Flood

When you see these symbols:

Read aloud
Read aloud to your child.

Read alone
Support your child as they read alone.

Read along
Read along with your child.

EGMONT
We bring stories to life

It was a beautiful morning in Pontypandy. The sun was shining, the birds were singing and in his bedroom over his mum's shop, Norman Price had just woken up.

Norman hated getting up early. He yawned and stretched as he pulled on his clothes, before shuffling over to his bedroom window.

When he pulled the curtains apart, Norman couldn't believe what he saw. Charlie's fishing boat was outside his bedroom window!

Read alone

Norman Price woke up. He was surprised to see a boat outside his window!

Read aloud   **Read along**

Norman ran downstairs to find his mum standing on the shop counter with water all around. "Mam!" he told her, "I think the whole town is flooded!'

Dilys thought for a moment. "You'd better get back upstairs," she said. "I'll ring the Fire Station to find out what to do."

But Norman had other things on his mind. "Do you think Woolly and Lambikins will be all right in their field?" Norman asked.

"I'm sure they'll be fine," Dilys said as she searched a shelf for her mobile phone.

Read alone

A bad flood had hit Pontypandy!
Norman was worried about his pet sheep.

Read aloud Read along

Meanwhile, up in Wallaby One, Fireman Sam and Tom Thomas were flying across Pontypandy, looking down at the damage.

"This is the worst high tide I've ever seen," Sam told Tom.

"And it won't go out again for four hours," Tom replied as he looked at the water below. It stretched from the Quayside to the centre of the town and beyond.

"I think we're going to have a busy day!" Sam said.

Sam and Tom flew over the town in a helicopter.
They were ready to rescue anyone in trouble.

Read alone

Read aloud **Read along**

Just then, Wallaby One's radio crackled and Station Officer Steele's voice boomed out.

"The Jones family went onto their roof to escape the flood," he told Sam and Tom. "Now they are stuck and need help getting to safety."

"We're on our way, Sir!" Sam replied as Tom steered Wallaby One towards the Quayside.

Station Officer Steele called Sam and Tom. The Jones family needed help.

Read alone

Read aloud   **Read along**

When they arrived at the Wholefish Café,
Sam bravely lowered himself down from
Wallaby One in a special harness.

"Is everyone all right?" Sam asked.

"We're OK," Bronwyn replied. "But we can't
find Lion!"

"I'm sure he'll be fine — he's a clever cat," said Sam.
"Let's get you all back to the station."

And so, one by one, Sam winched the Jones
family to safety.

Read alone

Sam rescued the Jones family from their roof.
But they couldn't find their cat, Lion.

Read aloud   Read along

At the same time, Penny and Elvis
were steering Neptune through the
flooded streets to help anyone in need.
They found Trevor stranded on top of his bus.

"I'm glad to see you!" Trevor said as he
wriggled down and landed softly on
board Neptune.

The three of them set off towards
the Fire Station.

Trevor Evans was trapped on the roof of his bus. Penny and Elvis took Neptune, the lifeboat, to rescue him.

Read aloud   Read along

Back in his bedroom, Norman was still worried about Woolly and Lambikins.
As he gazed out of his window towards their field, something caught his eye. A small rowing boat had drifted under his window. Norman looked at it for a moment and an idea popped into his head.

"I'll go to the field and save them myself!" he said aloud. Soon he was shimmying down a rope made of knotted bedsheets, into the boat.

Read alone

A rowing boat floated under Norman's window.
He decided to use it to save his sheep.

Read aloud   Read along

As Norman rowed the boat through Pontypandy, he heard a noise.

Meow! Norman stopped rowing ...

Meow! There it was again ...

Meow! Norman looked around and saw Lion floating on an upturned dustbin lid. He helped the poor little cat into his boat, and then he set off to save Woolly and Lambikins.

Norman rowed through Pontypandy.
He found Lion and put him safely in his boat.

Read alone

Read aloud   Read along

Penny, Elvis and Trevor were sailing past the shop in Neptune when Dilys rushed out. "Help!" she called. "Norman's disappeared!"

In a panic, Trevor jumped down from Neptune. "Don't worry, Dilys!" he said. "I'm here to help!"

But Dilys wasn't listening. "He was worried about Woolly and Lambikins," she told Penny and Elvis. "I think he may have gone to save them!"

"We need to talk to Wallaby One!" gasped Penny as she grabbed the lifeboat's radio. "Penny to Sam … do you hear me?"

Norman's mum found out he was missing!
She told Penny, who called Sam for help.

In Wallaby One, Sam and Tom were back in the air after dropping the Jones family at the Fire Station. "Reading you loud and clear, Penny. What's the problem?"

"Norman has gone out alone in the flood water to look for his sheep," Penny said over the radio.

"OK, Penny, we'll start a search operation from up here while you and Elvis search from Neptune," Sam said calmly. And with that, Tom swooped Wallaby One back over the town and towards the fields.

A search began. Sam used the helicopter to search from the air while Penny used Neptune to search the streets.

Read aloud   **Read along**

Back in his rowing boat, Norman had finally found Woolly and Lambikins and pulled the two sheep into the boat. But the little lamb was scared and wouldn't stop rushing around. The boat began to rock and sway ...

"Stay still, Lambikins!" Norman said as he reached for his oars. But his weight unbalanced the boat even more and he toppled overboard!

Splash!

Norman rescued Woolly and Lambikins.
But then he fell into the water!

Norman splashed around in the cold water.

"Help!" he shouted as loudly as he could, but there was no one around to hear him. As he thrashed around in the water, the boat began to drift away from him, taking Woolly, Lambikins and Lion with it.

Read alone

Norman called for help but no one could hear him. The boat began to float away.

Read aloud   Read along

Up in Wallaby One, Sam and Tom were zooming across the bay when they saw something below. It was Norman!

Sam grabbed the radio. "Sam to Penny," he said. "Norman is in the water at Breaker's Field. This is an emergency!"

"Penny to Sam," came her reply. "We'll get there straight away!"

Back in Neptune, Elvis and Dilys held on tightly as Penny cranked the lifeboat's engine up to full speed. Soon they were skimming across the water towards Breaker's Field.

From the helicopter, Sam saw Norman in the water. He told Penny where Norman was.

Read aloud   Read along

When they saw Norman, Penny slowed down before Elvis pulled him out of the water.

"It's a good job you're wearing your lifejacket, Norman," said Penny.

"Thanks for saving me," he replied. "But we need to get Woolly, Lambikins and Lion, too!" The animals were still floating out to sea!

Penny whizzed to the rescue! The animals were very scared, but Norman spoke to them softly as Penny gently lifted them into the lifeboat. They were safe at last!

Penny and Elvis raced to rescue Norman.
They saved the animals, too.

Read alone

Read aloud   Read along

Back at the Fire Station, everyone was pleased to see Norman and the animals safe and well. The tide was going out, and the flood waters were going down.

"You shouldn't have gone out in the flood," Station Officer Steele told Norman sternly. "You were in real danger out there."

"But you were very brave for saving the animals," Fireman Sam said, kindly, "even if we had to save you in the end!"